His Father's Song

Jessica Justus

Trilogy Christian Publishers
A Wholly Owned Subsidary of Trinity Broadcasting Network
2442 Michelle Drive
Tustin, CA 92780

Cover design by: Cornerstone Creative Solutions

For information, address Trilogy Christian Publishing
Rights Department, 2442 Michelle Drive, Tustin, Ca 92780.
Trilogy Christian Publishing/ TBN and colophon are trademarks of Trinity Broadcasting Network.

For information about special discounts for bulk purchases, please contact Trilogy Christian Publishing.

Manufactured in the United States of America

Trilogy Disclaimer: The views and content expressed in this book are those of the author and may not necessarily reflect the views and doctrine of Trilogy Christian Publishing or the Trinity Broadcasting Network.

10 9 8 7 6 5 4 3 2 1

Library of Congress Cataloging-in-Publication Data is available.

ISBN 978-1-68556-925-9 (Print Book)
ISBN 978-1-68556-926-6 (ebook)

Dedication

I am thankful and want to honor my parents and family, who have taught me to walk with Jesus through every storm. I hope this book encourages you!

I could hear the sound of the wind whistling through the trees when I heard the sound of thunder. The wind would blow through the branches of an old oak tree and rattle the leaves. Many storms would come and go and pass through, shaking the old tree at the top of the hill. Many times, as I walked by the old tree, I would hear the father oak tree singing to the acorns on the tree. Without fail every morning, the father would sing over the acorns. The acorns on the tree grew strong while the father sang over them. The father would sing to the acorns every day:

Drip, drip, drop, the rain will fall, but I stand strong and tall.
Drip, drip, drop, from the mountain top the wind will blow,
and you'll know how strong you are.
The rain will come, the wind will blow, but show the storm who you are.
Be strong and mighty when the wind roars.

On one of the branches closest to the trunk was an acorn named Aaron. Every morning, the father would whisper to Aaron, "Do not worry—you will be strong! I believe in you! I will never be too far away. Be strong and courageous, because one day you will become a strong oak tree, and people will depend on you. Laugh at the wind, because one day you will be loved by so many.

"Ha, ha, ha," his father would laugh and shout to the sky. His father was not afraid and would tease the wind. His father would remind him, "Soon enough, you will be a giant that stretches to the sky." Although Aaron loved his father and could hear his father's belief in him, the shaking and growling of the wind at night would scare him.

Each morning, Aaron was awakened by his father's song. While his father was singing, he was eager to be like him. Aaron would look into the distance without fear of the wind or storms. Aaron wanted to make his father proud.

The father's branches began to grow and spread out further and further. Aaron wasn't as close to the trunk of the tree anymore. He could still hear the song of his father:

Drip, drip, drop, the rain will fall, but I stand strong and tall.
Drip, drip, drop, from the mountain top the wind will blow,
and you'll know how strong you are.
The rain will come, the wind will blow, but show the storm who you are.
Be strong and mighty when the wind roars.

4

The leaves of the father oak tree would sway with the cold, bitter wind. The sky was usually painted with an array of colors, forming a beautiful painting, but this night would be much different.

Suddenly, during the night, thunder began to shake the sky, and lightning filled the air. The air was so thick, you could cut it like butter. A drumbeat filled the night sky, and it was terribly strong. The sound of the beating drum began to make Aaron shiver and the ground shake. He felt with each stroke of the drum that his strength was fading away. The wind felt as if it was continually choking Aaron while he was being tossed back and forth. Aaron could no longer hear the whisper of his father, only the growing, hissing sound of the wind. The wind was coiling around the branch like a snake and shook the branch fiercely. Aaron knew his father was very strong, but he was gasping for air and knew that his own strength could not hold him on much longer.

Whoosh! *Bam*! There was a final slam that cracked the branch. The wind persisted and began to get stronger and stronger. It was becoming harder to remember how strong his father was, because the wind had become louder and stronger over time. Aaron became very frightened and wrestled with the wind. The gust of wind swung at him from the right, then the left, and it slapped him in the face. "I don't know how much longer I can hold on," said Aaron. He began to get very tired. "Help me!" cried Aaron. "Help me!"

Aaron remembered that the voice of his father had strengthened him, but now, without hearing his father's voice, he had lost all will to fight. When all of his strength was gone Aaron was overpowered by the wind, and a strong burst knocked the air out of Aaron, causing him to spiral and tumble down to the ground at great speed.

As Aaron was twirling through the air he could hear the *chuck, chuck, chuckling* of the wind, snickering as he went diving through the air. The wind thought that he had won, but little did the wind know. This little acorn was about to begin a journey that would prepare him to be a giant oak tree.

Thump! *Thump*! *Thump*! Aaron hit the ground with great force and tumbled through the mud, swirling, swishing, and spinning, until he lost sight of his father. The trickling stream of water had turned into what felt like a rushing, rapid river, moving through the rocks and mud. Losing all control, Aaron was carried in the gushing river of water, drifting endlessly over the bumpy rocks, only moments later to find himself soaring through the air to plummet into another pile of mud.

Aaron now felt as if all had been lost. He gazed up at where the tall, towering oak tree had once been, wishing he could be back on the branch. Aaron had never thought it was possible for it to be so dark.

He was surrounded by the tall blades of grass, a stone wall, and the sounds of creatures in the field. How would he ever find his way out of this maze? Aaron felt like he had been whipped and beaten by the storm, with no return. How high up and close to the sun he had been. The brutal wind now felt even stronger and fiercer as it whipped through the blades of grass. He wished he could be back up on the branch, under the shelter of his father and the quilted blanket of leaves.

Aaron tried to remain encouraged and to remember what his father sang:

Drip, drip, drop, the rain will fall, but I stand strong and tall.
Drip, drip, drop, from the mountain top the wind will blow,
and you'll know how strong you are.
The rain will come, the wind will blow, but show the storm who you are.
Be strong and mighty when the wind roars.

Now his only friends were the rocks around him, the stone wall, and the hidden creatures in the field. Whose voice would guide Aaron now? If only a shadow of his father's words remained on the inside, he hoped they would be his guiding force to help him find strength within.

Being shattered on the inside, he felt the words of his father had disappeared. As Aaron sat in the darkness, he wondered, "How could I have fallen so low? How could I have ended up so far away? Where is my father?" Aaron, full of despair, covered in mud, and hiding in the darkness, was now hit by another storm. "Not again!" cried Aaron.

He had thought it was over, but now a storm of another kind had come. He was hit and tossed by some great force and landed in the mud again. He wished he could make a bed out of the mud and dirt and hide from the world.

Quickly approaching were great crowds of people, passing him by. He felt so small and tiny as they walked by. Aaron began to get lonely and started to sing, but no one responded. Aaron began to shout, but no one would listen. Aaron wondered, "Why does no one see me or listen to me?"

As time went by, not only did no one listen to him or see him, but people began to kick him and step on him as they walked by. Everybody was busy trying to get to their destinations; they could not see him. The people rushed by and didn't realize they were stepping on him. "Ouch!" screamed Aaron. Aaron was being tossed back and forth and was beginning to feel dizzy as he twirled in circles. It was hard to see, and he was beginning to feel confused as he was getting hit and kicked from all sides. Aaron thought that his misery was coming to an end, but unfortunately, this was the beginning of a treacherous trail for Aaron.

Aaron had experienced all that he thought he could handle, when a final hit from a man stepping on him pushed him into the bottomless, deep pit within the soil. Aaron tried with all his strength, but he could not get out. He felt crushed and full of despair. When he thought there could be no more pain, another storm came.

Aaron burst into tears, and he cried and cried until he thought he could not cry anymore. He missed his father, and he missed the warmth of the sun. He felt broken on the inside, and then he began to crack on the outside. Beat and broken, he sat in despair in his quiet, dark pit.

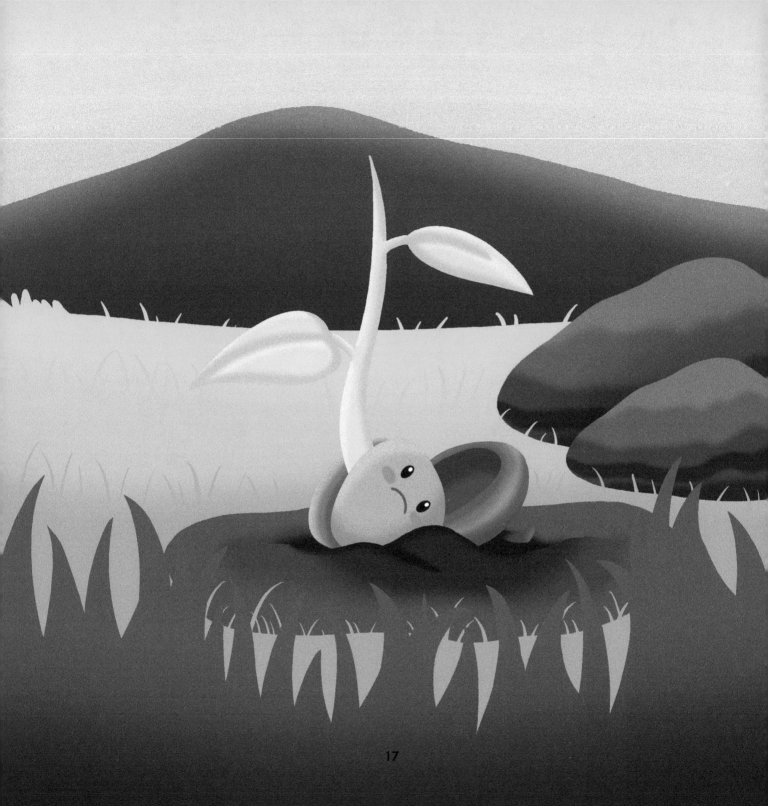

Time went by, and Aaron began to grow within the pit of the ground. Seasons would come and go, and the space Aaron was in began to feel smaller and smaller. He continued to grow, to break the ground, and to push through the soil. For the first time in a long time, the sun and spring breeze began to awaken Aaron.

Aaron believed that he had finally overcome the darkness, and that he was going to be able to overcome any storm. "I am going to be a giant! I am going to be a giant!" Inch by inch, Aaron grew. He grew taller and stronger. "I am becoming like my father too!" Days passed and turned into weeks, and then months, as Aaron continued to grow and sprout leaves.

One day, a man who frequently passed by paused, as if seeing Aaron for the first time, and he began to look and admire his tall trunk and long branches. "What a magnificent tree you will be!" said the man. Many days went on, and each time the man would stop and admire the tree.

Then one day, the man came back, and he began to admire and look closely at Aaron. Aaron loved it when the man would stay for a little while and rest from his walk. Winter had been cold and hard, leaving Aaron with a weight of dead leaves on his branches. The man began to cut away the dead leaves. Aaron, shocked, screamed in agony, "Ouch, that hurt!" The man removed the old, so Aaron could continue to grow strong. Aaron did not understand that the man was trying to help him grow.

The storms came again and seemed to beat Aaron with each drop of rain. He felt like he was drowning. For what seemed like endless weeks it rained, and rained, and rained. The rain and wind crashed onto Aaron as he kept standing and growing. As the rain beat against Aaron, he began to laugh at the storm and tell himself, "I will grow, grow, grow. I am planted deep, deep, deep, and I am going to be a strong oak tree. I am going to be a giant!"

The rain finally began to clear, and the clouds disappeared. The sun began to shine, and for the first time in a long time, Aaron could hear the music in the air and the song of his father:

Drip, drip, drop, the rain will fall, but I stand strong and tall.
Drip, drip, drop, from the mountain top the wind will blow,
and you'll know how strong you are.
The rain will come, the wind will blow, but show the storm who you are.
Be strong and mighty when the wind roars.

As the storm cleared, Aaron began to look across the field, and he could see his father and many other big strong oak trees. Time had passed, and he had not realized that during the storms he had become a strong, tall oak tree.

Aaron began to say, "I have become a giant! I have become a giant!" As months went by, people began to gather under the shade and strength of Aaron's branches and leaves. On hot summer days, people could find refuge and rest. On stormy winter days, Aaron became a refuge from the storm. Aaron no longer feared the storm and stood tall and strong when the wind and rain crashed against his branches. He knew that he was deeply rooted and would not be destroyed by the storm. The father was right—he was not alone, and people depended on him.

When Aaron realized that he had become a strong oak tree, he began to sing to all the growing oak trees around him his father's song:

Drip, drip, drop, the rain will fall, but I stand strong and tall.
Drip, drip, drop, from the mountain top the wind will blow,
and you'll know how strong you are.
The rain will come, the wind will blow, but show the storm who you are.
Be strong and mighty when the wind roars.

"Be strong, little ones, because one day you will be a big oak tree, and people will depend on you. Laugh at the wind, because one day you will be loved by so many. Soon enough, you will be a giant that stretches to the sky." Aaron smiled as he realized that his father was on the inside of him, and that was why he stood tall and strong.

Today, Aaron still remains at the top of that hill, and he waits for his many friends to come and sit under his branches to hear his father's song. Many tired travelers and friends have come along over the years, needing a little encouragement to remember who they are and who is on the inside of them. As people come, Aaron sings his father's song in the echo of the storm.

> "God so loved the world that he gave his one and only Son. Anyone who believes in him will not die but will have eternal life" (John 3:16 NIRV).

Prayer:

Jesus, thank You that You love me and that You died on the cross for me. I thank You that You gave Your life for me, and that because of Your death on the cross and resurrection from the grave I can have friendship with You. I thank You that You went up to the Father in heaven and sent the Holy Spirit to earth as my Helper. I know that while we wait for Your return, I can put my trust in You and develop a friendship with You through the Holy Spirit and the Bible.

I thank You that because of Your suffering and sacrifice, I can be washed clean and set free from all of my mistakes and sin. Your death paid the price for my sin and failures. You bought me with a price, and Your death on the cross and resurrection from the grave allows me to receive new life and joy. Jesus, I receive Your joy, love, and forgiveness.

You have accepted me and called me Your own. I thank You that I can have friendship with You and know You by praying and reading the Bible every day. I thank You that every time I pray, I can know that You hear me and You love me. Thank You for coming into my heart, life, and mind, and for never leaving me.

Thank You that You are seated in heaven at the right hand of the Father, and that You have sent the Holy Spirit to help me every day. Thank You for continually loving me, guiding me, and never leaving me. Thank You for being my Savior.

CPSIA information can be obtained
at www.ICGtesting.com
Printed in the USA
BVHW021506171022
649628BV00002B/76